A KEYBOARD ANTHOLOGY · THIRD SE
Edited by Howard Ferguson

BOOK V

1
ALLEMANDE

from French Suite No. 4 in E flat

J. S. BACH, BWV 815

Source: the text is based mainly on that given in the *Anna Magdalena Bach Notenbüchlein* of 1722, which Bach compiled for the use of his second wife; but some alternative readings from other manuscripts have been preferred. The dynamics are editorial. H.F.

2
LE COUCOU
(The Cuckoo)
Rondeau

DAQUIN

Source: Daquin's *1er. Livre de Pièces de Clavecin*, 1735. All phrase marks and dynamics are editorial. H.F.

3
SONATA in G

SCARLATTI, K.2, L.388

Presto [♩. = c.76]

Source: Scarlatti's *Essercizi per gravicembalo*, [1738]. All phrase marks and dynamics are editorial. H.F.

8

4
ALLEGRO

Third movement of Sonata in D minor

C. P. E. BACH, Wq. 57/4

Allegro [♩ = c. 69]

Source: C. P. E. Bach's *Clavier-Sonaten nebst einigen Rondos fürs Fortepiano, für Kenner und Liebhaber . . . dritte Sammlung*; Leipzig 1781.

A.B.1781

5
MINUET in D

MOZART, K.355

This Minuet, which is much later than its Köchel number would suggest, was probably written in 1790, the year before Mozart's death. As the autograph has not survived, the present text is based on the 1st edition of c.1798. A few editorial marks have been added within square brackets. The poignant mood of the piece requires a slower tempo than is usual for a minuet. H.F.

6
RONDO in A

BEETHOVEN, WoO 49

Source: *Neue Blumenlese für Klavierliebhaber:* Bossler, Speier [1784].
A.B.1781

7
SONG WITHOUT WORDS

MENDELSSOHN, Op.102, No. 3

Source: Mendelssohn's *Lieder ohne Worte*; Novello Ewer, London [n.d.]. The quavers throughout should be staccato, unless slurred. H.F.

8
IMPROMPTU
No. 1 of 'Albumblätter'

SCHUMANN, Op. 124, No. 1

Source: Schumann's *Albumblätter*, Op. 124, composed between 1832 and 1845.

9
PRELUDE in A flat

CHOPIN, B.86

Presto [♩ = c.100]
con leggierezzo

The autograph of this Prelude was dated 10 July 1834 but remained unpublished until it appeared in a Swiss magazine in August 1918. Though not included in many editions, there is no doubt about its authenticity. H.F.

A.B.1781

10
No. 2 of FIVE HUNGARIAN FOLKSONGS

LISZT, S.245

Source: Liszt's *Fünf Ungarische Melodien . . . im leichten Style bearbeitet;* Táborszky & Parsch, Budapest 1873.

11
WALTZ in E

BRAHMS, Op. 39, No. 2

Andante [♩ = c. 96]

Brahms' 16 *Walzer*, Op. 39, were originally written for piano duet; but he himself made the solo piano version. H.F.

A.B.1781

12
RUMORES DE LA CALETA
Malagueña
No. 6 of Recuerdos de viaje

ALBÉNIZ, Op. 71, No. 6

[Allegretto, ♪ = c.152]

Source: Albéniz' *Recuerdos de viaje;* Union Musicale Franco-Espagnole, Paris 1929.

A.B.1781

13
BERCEUSE

ILYNSKY, Op. 13, No. 7

14
PRELUDE in E minor

SKRYABIN, Op.11, No.4

Lento ♩ = 72-80

A.B.1781

Printed in England by Caligraving Limited Thetford Norfolk